A TIDEWATER PLACE

PORTRAIT OF THE WILLAPA ECOSYSTEM

BY EDWARD C. WOLF

PUBLISHED BY THE WILLAPA ALLIANCE

*The members of The Willapa Alliance are pleased to present this publication.
Willapa Bay is a national treasure, one of the cleanest large estuaries in the continental
United States. Our purpose in producing* A Tidewater Place *is to introduce you to this beautiful
and complex ecosystem and to encourage you to love and respect it as we do. This treasure is everyone's
treasure—aesthetically, environmentally and economically. We believe that providing
information such as this book is one of the keys to keeping Willapa
a beautiful, healthy and sustainable resource.*
—THE WILLAPA ALLIANCE

Published by The Willapa Alliance
in cooperation with The Nature Conservancy and Ecotrust
The Willapa Alliance
P.O. Box 773, Long Beach, WA 98631

Manufactured in the United States of America

Library of Congress information available
ISBN 0-89886-400-3

Written by Edward C. Wolf
Edited by Gordon Todd
Book/cover design by Elizabeth Watson
Map and chart illustrations by Vikki Leib, Charles Reidy
Original research by Kathleen Sayce, Michael Colby, Bruce Suzumoto, Rachel Nugent
Editorial assistance by Erin Kellogg, Rachel Bard
Willapa Alliance coordination by Dan'l Markham
Printed by United Graphics, Kent, Washington
Printed on Simpson Evergreen paper containing recycled fiber

Distributed by The Mountaineers Books, 1011 S.W. Klickitat Way, Suite 107,
Seattle, WA 98134, Phone: 800-553-4453, FAX: 206-223-6306

Front cover: Winter sunset over Willapa Bay, Washington (KEITH LAZELLE)
Contents page: A least sandpiper forages in shallow water (SUNNY WALTER)
Back cover: A great blue heron flies over Willapa Bay (STEVE TERRILL)

CONTENTS

PACIFIC OCEAN

N
W E
S

Grays Harbor

Aberdeen

HWY 12

Chehalis   *River*

HWY 105

HWY 101

North   *River*

GRAYS HARBOR CO

Shoalwater
Indian
Reservation

Tokeland

Raymond   *Willapa*

LEWIS CO

PACIFIC CO

Willapa Bay

Bone R.

South Bend

River

Bay Center

*Leadbetter
Point*

Niawiakum R.

WILLAPA HILLS

HWY 6

Pe Ell

Oysterville

*Long
Island*

Long Beach Peninsula

Nahcotta
Ocean Park

HWY 101

Middle Nemah River

WASHINGTON

Naselle

WAHKIAKUM CO

Naselle   *River*

Grays River

0   miles   5
0   km   5

Long Beach

Seaview

Bear River

HWY 101

HWY 4

Ilwaco

Knappton

Chinook

Columbia   River

Willapa Ecosystem
Willapa National Wildlife Refuge
Other State, Federal, and Private Protected Areas

Astoria

HWY 30

OREGON

WILLAPA ECOSYSTEM

INTRODUCTION

❧

Willapa is a tidewater place, renewed by natural cycles of departure and return. Each day Willapa Bay is cleansed by Pacific tides, each winter the Willapa Hills are replenished by the rains, and each year the tideflats and streams are visited by migrating salmon and shorebirds in their multitudes. Willapa's cycles are human as well, geared to the growth and harvest of natural products and linked to economic tides of supply and demand. In Willapa, the land, the waters, and the lives of people are inseparable.

❧ *Some 47,000 acres of mudflats are exposed at low tide in Willapa Bay.*
(MICHAEL PARKER)

5

LEFT: *The great blue heron hunts its prey in both saltwater and freshwater wetlands in the Willapa ecosystem.* (REX ZIAK)

ABOVE: *A narrow fringe of prairie-like saltmarsh. separates forested uplands from tidewater on the Bone River.* (SUNNY WALTER)

The Willapa Bay ecosystem—the estuary and the forested uplands whose fresh waters mix with the tidal surges of the bay—is the most productive coastal ecosystem remaining in the continental United States. One of every six oysters consumed in the United States grows on Willapa's tideflats. Pacific salmon, Dungeness crab, and several species of clams also abound in the bay. Nowhere in the Northwest do conifers grow faster, and cranberry bogs, cattle ranches, and dairy farms attest to the land's fertility.

Including the bay, the Willapa ecosystem encompasses some 680,000 acres in

6

the southwest corner of Washington state above the mouth of the Columbia River. Its forests of Douglas-fir, western hemlock, western redcedar and Sitka spruce once held some of the most massive trees encountered anywhere in the world. Its tidal flats make up a quarter of the productive shellfish-growing waters of the western United States. Its eelgrass beds and marshlands provide critical habitat for 70 species of migratory birds. The Willapa National Wildlife Refuge, established in 1938 to protect the winter habitat of a small sea goose called the Pacific or black brant, is one of the most ecologically diverse in the nationwide system of refuges. A partial roster of threatened or endangered species that still find a home in the refuge and elsewhere in the Willapa ecosystem includes at least 21 birds, 9 plants, 2 salamanders, a butterfly, and a snail.

Willapa's 19,000 year-round human residents depend on livelihoods rooted in the productive abundance of its lands and waters. Nearly two-thirds of the land in the Willapa Bay watershed is commercial forestland. Farms and irrigated lands together make up another seven percent, including the 1,400 acres of bogs in the Willapa area that account for virtually all of the state's harvest of cranberries. Oysters are cultivated on nearly 10,000 acres of privately owned or leased tidelands, and three species of Pacific salmon that return to spawn in Willapa's streams are caught by commercial fishermen in the open waters of the bay.

In short, the Willapa ecosystem is the base of the local economy. Without the forestlands and tideflats, without the restorative rhythms of departure and return, the livelihoods that have shaped Willapa's human history and that hold its hopes for the future could not exist. The continuing vitality of Willapa Bay, when most comparable ecosystems show signs of decline, is no coincidence. Far from urban centers, Willapa's population grew slowly. Since the first days of settlement, livelihoods in Willapa have been based on renewable resources that respond to careful management. The ecosystem's exceptional regenerative capacity has largely healed the scars of past abuse. Today, Willapa's residents are taking active steps to sustain the bay and its uplands, so that this natural endowment remains productive and beautiful for future generations. This is the story of the Willapa ecosystem: its natural history, its human history, and how local residents are shaping its future.

🌿 *Hemlock, ferns, and oxalis find shelter beneath a western redcedar in the Long Island Cedar Grove, part of the Willapa National Wildlife Refuge.*
(GARY BRAASCH)

SHAPED BY THE SEA
AND THE PASSAGE OF TIME,
WILLAPA BAY IS CONSIDERED
ONE OF THE CLEANEST
AND MOST PRODUCTIVE
LARGE ESTUARIES IN THE
UNITED STATES.

NATURAL HISTORY

*T*he Willapa ecosystem as it exists today has been shaped by the sea and the passage of time. Fifty million to 10 million years ago, the Pacific Ocean extended east as far as the present position of the Cascade Range. As the Cascades were uplifted, the coastline gradually retreated westward. Material from the young, volcanically active range accumulated offshore, punctured by volcanic vents through which basaltic and andesitic rocks joined the complex layer of sediments. During the past 10 million years, the release of

❦ LEFT: Willapa's mudflats bear the signature of the tides. (MICHAEL PARKER)

❦ ABOVE: Stretching south from Leadbetter Point, the Long Beach Peninsula protects Willapa Bay from Pacific surf. (MICHAEL PARKER)

🌿 *ABOVE: A coastal fog
settles across ridges and
ravines of the Willapa Hills.
(JOEL ROGERS)* 🌿 *RIGHT: The
Niawiakim River estuary,
a state Natural Area Preserve,
contains some of the finest
saltwater wetlands remaining in
Washington state. (KEITH LAZELLE)*

volcanic energy changed the forces beneath the surface and the Earth's crust rebounded, lifting sediments from the sea to form the Willapa Hills.

Sea levels along the Northwest coast rose and fell during the ice ages of the past 100,000 years; terraces formed when sea levels were 30 to 50 feet higher than today have left prominent features along Willapa's eastern shoreline including Bay Center and Long Island. As recently as 12,000 years ago when continental glaciers reached their maximum extent, the coastline lay far to the west of the Willapa Hills. Rapid melting of these glaciers brought the sea to its current level some 8,000 years ago. The ocean flooded low-lying river valleys up and down the coast, creating wide bays pounded by Pacific surf. As the surf eroded headlands separating these bays, coastal currents and river outwash pushed sand spits north and south across their openings.

Winter storms washed sand north from the mouth of the Columbia River to form the Long Beach Peninsula. Over several thousand years, the peninsula partially enclosed Willapa Bay, a shallow estuarine bay covering 88,000 acres at mean high tide. Each falling tide drains roughly 45 percent of the bay's 56.6 million cubic feet of water into the Pacific Ocean between Leadbetter Point and Cape Shoalwater. Much of that outflow returns on the next tide, so a complete exchange of water in the bay may take from two to three weeks. Shallow and fairly salty, the Willapa estuary is more productive, and sustains more varieties of shellfish, than either the Columbia River estuary to the south or Grays Harbor to the north; some scientists consider it the most productive estuary in the continental United States.

Rain-laden clouds driven before the southwesterly storms of winter carry fresh water to the Willapa ecosystem. From 85 inches to as much as 200 inches of rain in some interior valleys soak Willapa's landscape each year, 90 percent of the rain falling between October and May. Rainfall drains into Willapa Bay through a rugged 600,000-acre watershed of ridges and steep-sided ravines carved by millions of years of runoff. The outflow of 1,470 miles of rivers and small streams within the drainage basin carries only a tiny fraction of the volume of water exchanged by the tides, though this flow carries nutrients to the estuary from the uplands, enriching the bay's web of life. The plume of the Columbia River, pushed

❧ OVERLEAF: Many shorebirds, including dunlin, migrate through Willapa. (ART WOLFE) ❧ ABOVE: Western redcedars on Long Island are among the state's oldest trees. (REX ZIAK) ❧ RIGHT: Saltmarshes filter runoff of Willapa's tributaries. (KEITH LAZELLE)

north during the winter by prevailing winds, can measurably dilute the bay, and its waters also bring large amounts of sediment.

Some 47,000 acres of mudflats are exposed at low tide, and much of the remainder of Willapa Bay lies less than six feet below low water. On the intertidal and subtidal mudflats, extensive beds of a native eelgrass *(Zostera marina)* support a whole sub-system of life. The delicate eelgrass plants support communities of epiphytes—tiny non-parasitic plants that grow on the eelgrass blades. So numerous are these microscopic plants that they may approach the weight of the plant that supports them. Complex communities of microbes also found in eelgrass beds help recycle phosphorus and nitrogen, critical nutrients of the food web in the bay. Young fish hunt and forage in these eelgrass "pastures," and the grass itself supplies the main food of waterfowl including black brant *(Branta bernicla nigricans)* and American widgeon *(Anas americana)*.

An extraordinary assemblage of fish, shellfish, and marine mammals finds food and habitat in the shallows of the bay. Anadromous fish—migratory species that enter freshwater streams from the ocean to spawn—including salmon, steelhead, sea-run cutthroat trout, sturgeon, and smelt all reproduce in Willapa's streams and mature in the bay. Herring and flatfish enter the bay from the Pacific Ocean to lay their eggs in the eelgrass beds. Young Dungeness crabs *(Cancer magister)* develop on Willapa's oyster beds before migrating out of the bay to deep water at age two. Harbor seals *(Phoca vitulina)* fish in Willapa's waters, and on occasion, gray whales *(Eschrichtius robustus)* swim in to feed on zooplankton, shrimp, and herring eggs.

At the mouths of the larger rivers within the reach of tidewater, prairie-like saltmarshes shelter waterfowl and provide forage for elk that come down from the hills during the winter months. These native marshes also filter runoff from the uplands and release fine plant debris to the mudflats where clams, oysters, and other filter-feeding invertebrates grow fat on algae and plankton in the nutrient-rich waters.

Three of the five native species of Pacific salmon remain relatively abundant in Willapa. Chum salmon *(Oncorhyncus keta)*, historically most numerous, prefer spawning grounds near tidewater in nearly all the rivers and streams that are tributary to the bay. Coho (silver) salmon *(Oncorhyncus kisutch)* spawn in most of the

🌿 *TOP: Roosevelt elk graze tidewater marshes during the winter. (JOEL ROGERS)*
🌿 *BOTTOM: The federally threatened snowy plover nests near Leadbetter Point on the Long Beach Peninsula.*
(ROBERT ASHBAUGH)

streams and creeks, while chinook (king) salmon (*Oncorhyncus tshawytscha*) rely on extensive spawning grounds in the Naselle River as well as some streams in the Bear, Nemah, North, Palix, and Willapa drainages. Once they have left their natal streams, juvenile and adult salmon feed in the bay on anchovies, herring, and many kinds of zooplankton before moving out to the open ocean. Mature chinook salmon are the first to return to Willapa's waters each year, arriving in July and continuing to spawn through November. Coho salmon arrive in late August and spawn through December, while chum salmon appear in mid-September and complete their run by Thanksgiving.

The tidelands of Willapa Bay are an important rest stop for waterfowl and seabirds that follow a north-south migration route known as the Pacific Flyway. Willapa is likely to become even more critical to some species, including black brant and canvasbacks (*Aythya valisineria*), as San Francisco Bay and other wetlands along the Pacific Coast are diminished by development. A visitor to Leadbetter Point at the height of the spring migration may see as many as 35,000 shorebirds at one time; on a typical fall day, more than 80,000 southbound waterfowl forage on the tideflats of the bay.

Willapa lies near the midpoint of the great band of conifer rain forests that once stretched from the coastal redwoods of northern California to the spruce vistas of the Alaskan panhandle. With its mild, wet climate and fertile soils, Willapa supported some of the largest trees found in the Northwest. Though only a few small stands of old-growth forest remain, Willapa's upland second-growth forests of Douglas-fir and western hemlock still harbor Roosevelt elk, black bear, black-tailed deer, cougar, bobcat, coyote, raccoon, beaver, river otter, northern flying squirrels, and many smaller rodents and insect-eaters. Marbled murrelets (*Brachyramphus marmoratus*) nest in lowland redcedar-Sitka spruce stands found near the South Nemah River and on Long Island; Willapa is one of just a few confirmed nesting sites for this species in Washington state.

People have probably been an integral part of the ecosystem for as long as the Long Beach Peninsula has partially enclosed Willapa Bay. Several thousand years ago, Salish-speaking tribes moved down the coast from the north. Their cultures centered on abundant shellfish and salmon and on the cedar tree, once common in coastal forests, from which they fashioned shelter, clothing, and canoes. At Willapa Bay, the Chehalis Indian descendants of these peoples encountered Lower Chinook tribes whose villages bordered the bays and tidelands at the mouth of the Columbia River. The Chinooks were traders whose networks extended far up the coast into present-day British Columbia and into the continental interior beyond the Columbia Gorge. During the winter, they turned to seasonal camps on the lee side of the Long Beach Peninsula and along Willapa Bay to harvest oysters and clams.

By the late 18th century, Lower Chinook and Chehalis tribes living in the Willapa region may have numbered close to 9,000 people. About this time, Indians of mysterious origins came down the Willapa Valley speaking an Athabascan language unrelated to Salish or Chinook. The Chinooks called them Kwalhioqua, a name that means "in a lonely wooded place." Numbering only a few dozen, the Kwalhioqua assimilated into Chehalis and Chinook villages and nearly vanished as a distinct culture.

After 1829, epidemic disease introduced by European fur traders ravaged native villages along the lower Columbia River and in Willapa Bay in a tragedy of stunning proportions: Only 116 Chinook people remained when permanent white settlers began to arrive in the 1850s, and Lower Chehalis, Chinookan, and Kwalhioqua survivors amalgamated into a single community. In 1851, the survivors ceded their ancestral lands to the U.S. Government in treaties that were never ratified. A few dozen Chinook and Chehalis families refused relocation to the Quinault Reservation up the coast, and in 1866, President Andrew Johnson established by executive order the 335-acre Georgetown Indian Reservation (later renamed the Shoalwater Bay Indian Reservation) on a parcel of land (excluding tidelands) near Tokeland. The shadowy Kwalhioqua left one legacy that endures today: a name the whites rendered as "Willapa."

🌿 *Native Americans have harvested Willapa salmon for generations.* (SHOALWATER BAY INDIAN TRIBE COLLECTION)

SINCE THE FIRST
PERMANENT WHITE SETTLERS
ARRIVED, WILLAPA'S PRINCIPAL
LIVELIHOODS—OYSTER
HARVESTING, LOGGING, FISHING,
AND TOURISM—HAVE
REMAINED THE SAME.

TIDELANDS
TRANSFORMED

❦

On July 5, 1788, the Felice, a trading vessel of the British East India Company under the command of Lt. John Meares, encountered breakers at the mouth of an uncharted bay Meares recorded in the ship's log as "Shoalwater." As it lay at anchor off the bar, the Felice was approached by a native man and boy in a cedar canoe who offered two sea otter skins to the crew. Four years later, surf on the bar deterred Capt. George

19

❧ *LEFT: Many tidal inlets still resemble the shoreline first charted in 1852. (JOEL ROGERS)*

❧ *ABOVE: Bay Center has been a commercial oystering hub for more than a century. (GARY BRAASCH)*

🌿 *Settlers diked and drained
thousands of acres of marsh to
create productive pastureland.*

(GARY BRAASCH)

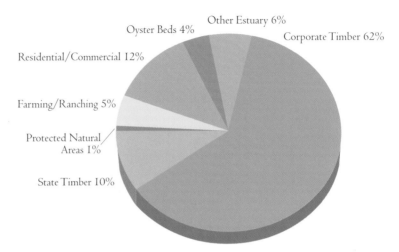

Oyster Beds 4%

Other Estuary 6%

Corporate Timber 62%

Residential/Commercial 12%

Farming/Ranching 5%

Protected Natural
Areas 1%

State Timber 10%

WILLAPA BAY ECOSYSTEM LAND USE

Vancouver from sailing into the bay. Left off the famous explorer's coastal charts, Shoalwater Bay attracted little attention for nearly six decades.

Lt. James Alden, commanding the U.S. coastal survey steamer Active, made the first detailed reconnaissance of the bay in 1852. Alden noted a handful of white settlers employed in oystering for the California market (the first deck cargo of oysters had been shipped by schooner to San Francisco not long before). When James Swan, who later chronicled the settlement of the bay, arrived the following year, he noted a few men felling giant trees on the Willapa River, and counted 14 whites and numerous Indians gathering oysters.

Swan had seen sawdust 30 miles at sea off the mouth of the Columbia on his journey to Shoalwater Bay, evidence even then of the burgeoning sawmills along that river, and of the gold-rush prosperity in a California that had begun to hunger for resources that lay to the north. Their fortunes tied to this California market, the ranks of Willapa's early settlers expanded slowly during the 1850s, most supporting themselves by harvesting oysters and cutting timber for the schooner trade. Some established farms on the marshy "prairies" that edged the Willapa River. The first settlements included Bruceport on the bay's eastern shore, and Oysterville on the Long Beach Peninsula, the first county seat of Pacific County.

By the 1870s, the peninsula had become a destination favored by tourists from the Portland area, but the inner shore of the bay remained sparsely settled.

In the 140 years since the first permanent white settlers arrived, Willapa's principal livelihoods—oyster harvesting, logging, fishing, and tourism—have remained the same. The scale of resource harvests, and the methods used to exploit the ecosystem's abundance, have changed dramatically. Two lifetimes have been enough to tame the Willapa ecosystem, marking a subtle but fundamental shift from a wild to a cultivated resource base.

OYSTERS

Oystering was the first of Willapa's industries to make the shift from dependence on a resource that could be gathered from the wild to one that was carefully farmed. During the first decades of settlement, native Olympia oysters (*Ostrea lurida*) on the tideflats seemed inexhaustible, and the easily harvested shellfish were taken with little thought for their renewal. The most accessible beds of Olympia oysters were depleted by the 1880s, and the shipment of oysters from Willapa Bay tapered off. The year 1894 marked an ecological milestone, as 80 barrels of non-native eastern oysters (*Crassostrea virginica*) were planted at the mouths of the Palix and Naselle Rivers in an effort to revive the dwindling trade.

Eastern oysters flourished, though they did not reproduce in Willapa's waters,

❧ Top: Oysters are gathered by hand on the tideflats, much as they were gathered by native Americans centuries ago. (Gary Braasch) ❧ Bottom: One of every six oysters eaten in the United States comes from Willapa. (Doug Plummer)

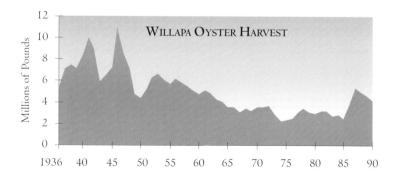

WILLAPA OYSTER HARVEST

Millions of Pounds

12 10 8 6 4 2 0

1936 40 45 50 55 60 65 70 75 80 85 90

21

and an annual infusion of juveniles of this species from the eastern seaboard revived oyster harvesting through the first two decades of the twentieth century. In 1919, however, an epidemic shellfish disease aided by unusual weather swept the tidelands, bringing the era of the eastern oyster in Willapa to an end. The Pacific oyster *(Crassostrea gigas)*, introduced to Willapa Bay from Japan in 1928, outgrew both the native and eastern species. For eight years, juvenile Pacific oysters ("spat") attached to oyster shells were imported from Japan, reviving the troubled industry. Then in 1936, Pacific oysters reproduced naturally ("set") in all parts of the bay. Though imports of spat continued into the 1970s, the introduced species had become a functional part of the Willapa ecosystem.

Oystering in Willapa Bay became increasingly scientific during the post-World War II decades, even as the total oyster harvest, which peaked at 10 million pounds in 1946, gradually declined to a low of just over 2 million pounds in 1974. The average size of oysters in Willapa also declined, slightly but measurably, during this period, particularly during the 1980s. Meanwhile, other non-native shellfish such as the Japanese littleneck clam (introduced accidentally with the seed of Pacific oysters) have taken hold in the tidelands, broadening the base of species that can be harvested in commercial quantities.

FORESTS

Though many early settlers came to Willapa to farm, most soon turned to cutting timber—a laborious but lucrative business. In the early 1850s, Douglas-fir timber in streamside stands could be felled directly into the Willapa River and floated to schooners anchored in the harbor. The logs were destined for San Francisco for use as harbor pilings and ship spars. In 1858, the first local sawmill opened on Mill Creek, a tributary of the Willapa River. During the latter decades of the 19th century, loggers used teams of oxen to haul logs to tidewater on corduroy "skid roads." Around 1900, steam power replaced the bull teams; "steam donkeys" and ground-lead cables were used to haul logs great distances through

❧ *LEFT: More than 60 percent of Willapa's timberlands have been logged since the end of World War II. (MICHAEL PARKER)*
❧ *ABOVE: Timber from second-growth forests now makes up more than 90 percent of Willapa's harvest. (REX ZIAK)*
❧ *OVERLEAF: A screen of red alder is reflected in the upper reach of tidewater. (RUTH TAYLOR)*

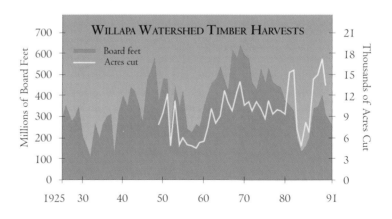

the forest, and logging for profit became Willapa's primary industry.

By World War I, private timber companies had constructed railroads up sections of the Willapa, North, Nemah, and Naselle River valleys to reach lush timber stands more distant from water. High-lead logging with cables strung from the tops of tall trees increased loggers' reach into the forest. Willapa lumber helped fuel the shipbuilding trade during the war, and loggers for the U.S. Army's Spruce Division felled straight-grain spruce during the winter of 1917, used to build the first generation of warplanes. A postwar housing boom kept demand for Willapa lumber strong throughout the 1920s.

Few roads existed in the Willapa watershed at that time, and loggers relied on the streams and rivers to move timber to mills and markets. Elaborate "splash dams," built by hand with the huge logs, were used to block streams and create temporary reservoirs in which logs could be floated. When the dam gates were opened, water and logs rushed downstream to tidewater in a destructive torrent. The first splash dam was built on the upper Willapa River in 1883, and the last one abandoned in 1940 when truck logging proved cheaper and faster. For over half a century, splash dams scoured stream channels and damaged natural salmon runs. By the time the splash dam era ended, the natural features of many miles of Willapa's streams had been dramatically changed.

By the 1930s, though plenty of big timber remained to be cut, the end of the virgin forest was in sight. Major timber companies including the

ABOVE: By the start of the 20th century, logging had become Willapa's primary industry.
(ILWACO HERITAGE FOUNDATION COLLECTION)

WILLAPA WATERSHED TIMBER HARVESTS

Weyerhaeuser Company began to consolidate large tracts of timberland to practice a new form of "sustained-yield" forestry that involved replanting and managing trees as a crop that could be harvested every 60 years from the same lands. Part of the Clemons Tree Farm, the first industrial tree farm in the United States, lies in the Willapa ecosystem.

World War II and postwar prosperity revived demand for the high-quality construction lumber that could be milled from Willapa's logs. The use of heavy tractors and chainsaws became standard practice, and a network of new logging roads opened remaining forest stands to truck logging. From 1949 to 1986, more than 340,000 acres of forest were logged in the Willapa Hills, yielding 14 billion board feet of lumber. Roughly six of every ten acres of forestland in the Willapa ecosystem were cut during the four decades spanning the transition from old-growth forest to industrial tree farm.

Willapa's timber harvest peaked in 1970, when 643 million board feet were cut; by then the old trees were nearly gone and the second-growth trees were far too small to harvest. Gradually, the timber industry shifted from reliance on old-growth logs toward smaller logs with different wood-fiber properties, and the harvest of hemlocks for pulp largely replaced the Douglas-fir sawtimber. In 1982, harvest from young second-growth stands exceeded the volume of harvest of old trees for the first time. Since then, big trees have made up less than ten percent of total timber harvests. Harvests in the late 1980s ranged from a quarter to slightly more than half the volume cut at the 1970 peak, as many young stands matured to harvestable size. The yield of wood has plunged sharply as well, from 42,000 to around 23,000 board feet per acre.

🍃 *A vigorous Douglas-fir branch combs moisture from the air.* (REX ZIAK)

SALMON

Commercial fishing, a smaller industry in Willapa Bay than in the Columbia River, has always been an integral part of the local economy. Salmon generally account for more than 90 percent of the finfish caught in Willapa's waters. As in

🌿 *Pacific salmon, primarily chinook and coho, account for more than 90 percent of the finfish caught in Willapa's waters.* (DOUG WILSON)

the Columbia River fishery, most of the salmon taken in Willapa during the early decades of settlement were caught in stationary fish traps. When fish traps were outlawed by the Washington state legislature in 1935, commercial gillnetting replaced them in the bay. Since the fish trap era, the annual catch of salmon has fluctuated widely, from as few as 25,000 to more than 200,000 fish.

Since 1899, when the first hatchery opened on the Willapa River, hatcheries have released salmon fry into Willapa streams. But not until the 1950s did coho and chinook salmon released from hatcheries began to augment natural runs of wild salmon in Willapa's streams on a large scale. Hatchery capacity doubled in 1980 with the opening of the Naselle River hatchery.

Natural runs of chum salmon, once the most abundant of Willapa's salmon but seldom propagated by state hatcheries and at times actively discouraged by fisheries managers, are now only 15 percent to 30 percent of their historical size; the annual chum run barely reaches 100,000 fish. Though the present runs of coho and chinook match and sometimes even surpass their historical runs in size, some 80 percent of the chinook salmon and 90 percent of the coho salmon caught in the bay are reared in hatcheries. Four state-run hatcheries have supplanted wild runs on hundreds of streams.

At one time each of those wild runs was genetically unique, distinct from all other salmon stocks in the ecosystem and the entire Northwest. With a hatchery-based fishery, that native genetic diversity is disappearing. Chinook and coho stocks from all over the region have been used to supply Willapa hatcheries with

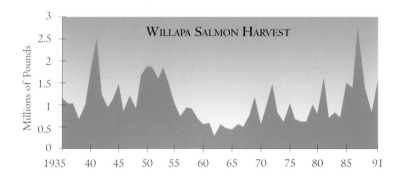

28

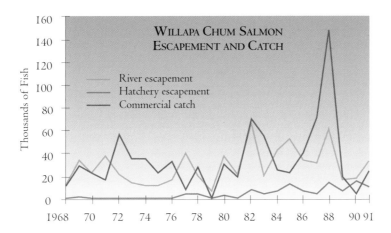

WILLAPA CHUM SALMON
ESCAPEMENT AND CATCH

River escapement
Hatchery escapement
Commercial catch

eggs. Salmon grown from these eggs interbreed extensively with Willapa's remaining wild salmon, gradually eroding their uniqueness. In 1991, the National Marine Fisheries Service identified Willapa coho salmon as a wild stock at high risk of extinction due to high offshore catch levels and interbreeding with hatchery stock.

❦ Commercial gillnetters and crabbers are integral parts of Willapa's economy. (JOEL ROGERS)

CRANBERRIES

Chinook Indians harvested native cranberries *(Vaccinium oxycoccos)* from natural sphagnum bogs north of the present site of Ilwaco on the Long Beach Peninsula for countless generations. Though the small native berries were never domesticated, they inspired an important chapter in Willapa's agricultural history. In 1883, just a decade before eastern oysters were planted on the tidelands, a settler from the East Coast introduced vines of several cranberry varieties then popular in New England to a cultivated bog near Long Beach.

Cultivation on a commercial scale began in the years just prior to World War I, when local farmers planted several hundred acres of bogs with vines from Cape Cod. By the 1930s, the cultivation of cranberries proved so successful that it

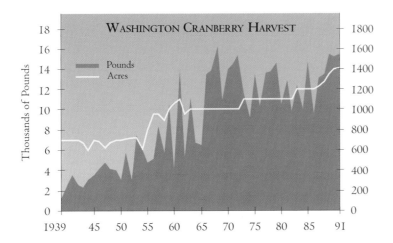

WASHINGTON CRANBERRY HARVEST

Pounds
Acres

ranked second only to dairying in the region's agricultural economy. Today cranberries are the most valuable food crop grown in the ecosystem.

The Willapa ecosystem today, still productive and lovely to behold, bears only superficial resemblance to the ecosystem that sustained the Chinook, Chehalis, and Kwalhioqua peoples. The tidelands continue to yield oysters in abundance—some four million pounds harvested in 1990—but the Pacific oyster has essentially replaced the native Olympia oyster in the six decades since its introduction. In the uplands, nine acres out of ten are now even-aged plantations of trees of less than 70 years old. Four acres in ten have been planted in just the last 20 years; never in the history of the Willapa ecosystem has such a vast share of its trees been so young. Each summer and fall, hundreds of thousands of chinook and coho salmon still return to the streams of the watershed thanks to hatchery enhancement, but most are not native salmon; they carry genes gleaned from salmon stocks all over the Northwest. Cranberries, first introduced in the Willapa watershed from Cape Cod over a century ago, have become Willapa's premier crop.

Willapa today is a farmed ecosystem, its uplands, tideflats, and fisheries cultivated according to human design. But farming remains a part of the larger system of nature, not apart from that system. As the following section relates, the vitality of some of Willapa's resource-based livelihoods can be threatened when nature's equilibrium is upset.

LEFT: Cranberries are the most valuable food crop grown in the Willapa ecosystem. (KEITH LAZELLE) *ABOVE: Cranberry bogs, flooded for harvest, present a crimson spectacle. (MICHAEL PARKER)*

UNLESS THE CURRENT
THREATS TO THE WILLAPA
ECOSYSTEM'S HEALTH ARE
RESOLVED, THE AREA'S ABILITY
TO SUPPORT ITS ACCUSTOMED
ABUNDANCE AND DIVERSITY
COULD BE LOST.

SIGNS OF STRESS

❧

Nature is dynamic, and even obvious physical changes in an ecosystem can defy simple cause-and-effect explanations. The diking and draining of coastal wetlands is a case in point. By 1977, some 6,177 of Willapa's 12,469 acres of shoreline wetlands had been diked, and a quarter of those diked acres had been filled. Though much of that acreage was diked and drained decades ago to create pastures, in recent years road-building and urban and industrial development have eliminated wetlands. The overall reduction of native

❧ *LEFT: Spartina, a cordgrass native to the East Coast, is a threat to Willapa's tidelands.* (*JOEL ROGERS*) ❧ *ABOVE: Patches of aggressive spartina turn tidelands to saltmarsh and displace native species.* (*MICHAEL PARKER*)

🐚 *TOP: By loosening bottom sediments, burrowing shrimp such as this ghost shrimp reduce the species diversity of eelgrass and oyster beds by nine-tenths. (GREGORY C. JENSEN)* 🐚 *BOTTOM: Research on burrowing shrimp may yield strategies for control. (BRETT DUMBAULD)*

tidal marshlands has diminished the productivity and filtering capacity of the Willapa ecosystem as a whole, but the consequences of this physical change for the health of the ecosystem are difficult to pinpoint.

Products harvested from a changing ecosystem tell another story. Declines in log diameters, the average size of oysters, and the numbers of salmon caught reveal that the Willapa ecosystem is changing, but tell little about the implications of those changes. Changes in the relative abundance of different species within an ecosystem ripple through its food webs, causing unexpected effects.

Ecological disruption occurs when a native species proliferates out of control to the point that it renders the ecosystem unsuitable for other species. Such has been the case with two types of shrimp unpalatable to people, mud shrimp (*Callianassa californiensis*) and ghost shrimp (*Upogebia pugettensis*), that burrow in mudflats in the intertidal zone of Willapa Bay. Mud shrimp loosen the surface, and ghost shrimp consume food preferred by oysters. Together, these burrowing shrimp render the tidelands less suitable for eelgrass, oysters, crabs, and many other marine inverte-brates. They can reduce the natural species diversity found in eelgrass and oyster beds by 80 percent to 95 percent.

The explosion of burrowing shrimp populations since the 1950s is not fully understood, but declining stocks of chum salmon (which are believed to consume the larvae of burrowing shrimp) and green and white sturgeon (which feed on the adult shrimp) may have released the shrimp from predation pressure. Burrowing shrimp continue to increase, and "shrimp deserts"—mudflats rendered unsuitable for other species by the action of the shrimp—now cover 20,000 acres. The abun-dance of burrowing shrimp jeopardizes the future of Willapa's oyster industry. Fewer than 10,000 acres of tidelands are now in oyster production—and no polit-ically acceptable means of controlling the shrimp has been found.

The unintended introduction of species alien to the ecosystem has provoked other changes as worrisome as the fluctuations of native species. The most visible example is the aggressive cordgrass, *Spartina alterniflora*, introduced from the East Coast in the 1890s, perhaps by accident (spartina was used to pack the spat-on-shell of eastern oysters planted at the mouth of the Palix River in 1894). A century later, it poses a serious threat to the tideland ecosystem.

Like most newcomers, spartina was not perfectly adapted to its new surroundings. For nearly six decades, spartina plants reproduced primarily by vegetative means, spreading slowly from established patches. Spartina began to set seed in large amounts in the 1960s, and new clumps separate from the parent plants began to appear. When surveyed in 1989, patches of spartina covered over 2,400 acres of mudflats near the high-tide line. Spartina displaces eelgrass in the intertidal zone, crowding out the many plant and animal species dependent on the eelgrass meadows. Its roots trap sediment, and thereby rapidly raise the elevation of tideflats, rendering them unsuitable for oyster production. Virtually all organisms that depend on eelgrass and mud are affected, including people whose livelihoods depend on the harvest of clams and oysters.

Spartina is now rapidly filling parts of the bay, narrowing the critical band between high and low tides. If its reproduction is not checked, spartina may turn as much as half of the bay's gently sloping mudflats into elevated saltmarsh in less than 20 years. Ultimately, three-quarters of the tidelands are at risk.

Ironically, Willapa's waters are cleaner today than a generation ago. Water quality improved as wastewater treatment and pollution control measures were adopted. Local concern for clean water is high. When Palix River oyster beds were closed to harvesting by state health officials several years ago due to high levels of fecal coliform (bacteria associated with human waste as well as various non-human sources), residents upgraded septic systems. In late 1992, the Palix beds were reopened for oyster harvest—the first time such harvest restrictions have been lifted in Washington state. Nesting pairs of bald eagles (*Haliaeetus leucocephalus*), top predators in the tideland food chain, have increased slightly in Willapa in recent years, their recovery suggesting improvement in the quality of their prey and habitat. Effective pollution control probably played a part in that increase.

Such changes demonstrate the resilience of the Willapa ecosystem and suggest that with cooperative effort even the proliferation of burrowing shrimp and spartina can be reversed. But unless these current threats to ecosystem health are confronted and resolved, the bay's ability to support its accustomed abundance and diversity of shellfish, finfish, and the species that depend on them—including people—could be lost.

35

Nesting pairs of bald eagles appear to be making a modest comeback in the Willapa ecosystem. (JEFFREY S. BOUCHER)

WILLAPA IS THE KIND OF PLACE WHERE A SUSTAINABLE ECONOMY—ONE THAT HARVESTS THE ABUNDANCE OF THE ECOSYSTEM WHILE MAINTAINING ITS DIVERSITY AND INTEGRITY—OUGHT TO BE POSSIBLE.

A SUSTAINABLE ECONOMY

❦

*T*he people of Willapa Bay recognize that a healthy ecosystem goes hand in hand with a healthy local economy. Many locally owned businesses on Willapa's lands and waters date back to the early days of settlement; families have participated directly in the transformations that have already unfolded here, and the commitment to environmental quality is deeply felt. Willapa is the kind of place where a sustainable local economy—one that harvests

❦ *LEFT: Sustainable livelihoods must honor the natural abundance and diversity of the ecosystem. (JOEL ROGERS)* ❦ *ABOVE: Oystering sets a standard for sustainable enterprises. (MICHAEL PARKER)*

the abundance of an extraordinary ecosystem while maintaining its diversity and integrity—ought to be possible.

Yet recent years have been difficult ones for Willapa's communities. The four counties that share the ecosystem (Pacific, Grays Harbor, Lewis, and Wahkiakum) are among the most economically depressed in Washington state. The number of timber and wood products jobs has declined continuously over the last several decades as automation has replaced manual tasks in the industry. Unemployment has exceeded the state average for at least the last 20 years, family incomes are low, and most young people leave Willapa for brighter prospects in urban areas when they graduate from high school.

The livelihoods that sustain Willapa's communities depend on the natural cycles that renew the productivity of the lands and waters. If people are to prosper without overtaxing that productivity, their economy must encourage and reward good resource management. With new insight into the workings of the ecosystem and new opportunities for cooperative problem-solving at the local level, a sustainable economy based on the ecosystem may be at hand.

Rural communities around the world face a common question: Can economic development restore balance to the ecosystem while bringing reasonable prosperity to local residents? As a place where answers might be found, Willapa possesses some unique advantages. The resident population has expanded slowly to its current level of about 19,000. The base of employment is relatively diverse, with just over a third of the area's 7,800 jobs in forest products, fisheries, and agriculture. Tourism, already a $15-million yearly business, makes a growing

🌿 TOP: *Nearly a century old, the Shelburne Inn in Seaview attracts visitors from all over the world.* (DOUG PLUMMER) 🌿 BOTTOM: *Solitude rewards hikers in the Willapa ecosystem.* (REX ZIAK)

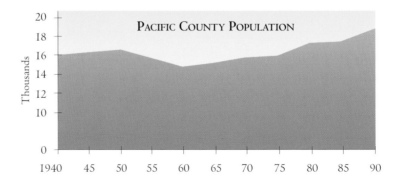

PACIFIC COUNTY POPULATION

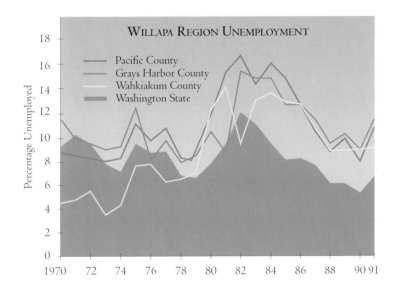

WILLAPA REGION UNEMPLOYMENT

Pacific County
Grays Harbor County
Wahkiakum County
Washington State

Percentage Unemployed

18
16
14
12
10
8
6
4
2
0

1970 72 74 76 78 80 82 84 86 88 90 91

contribution to local economies as Willapa's attractions of scenery, sportfishing, and undeveloped shoreline become scarcer in other parts of the Pacific Northwest.

The mainstays of Willapa's economy—shellfish, forest products, fish, agriculture, tourism, and retirement—depend directly on the health, productivity, and beauty of the ecosystem. Four of these industries depend on the harvest and sale of natural materials, and thus on the productive capacity of the lands and waters, while two depend on attracting people who bring money earned elsewhere to spend in the local economy.

Sustainable economic development will require adjustments in many of the resource-based industries within the Willapa ecosystem, from the timberlands to the tidelands, from dairy farms to cranberry bogs to beachfront vacation homes. Above all, it will require local choices and local decisions. As the examples that follow suggest, the cornerstones of sustainability have already been laid.

Oystering, the centerpiece of Willapa's tideland enterprises, actually enhances the diversity of the estuary. Oyster beds on the tideflats, and racks and lines on which oysters are also cultivated, provide habitat for crabs, eelgrass, algae, and many marine invertebrates essential to a healthy ecosystem. Oysters filter water as they feed, improving water quality for young fish in the shallows. Oystering suggests an

❧ *TOP: Kite festivals capitalize on steady sea breezes. (WAYNE O'NEIL)*
❧ *BOTTOM: The peninsula's outer beach can still inspire wonder. (STEVE TERRILL)*

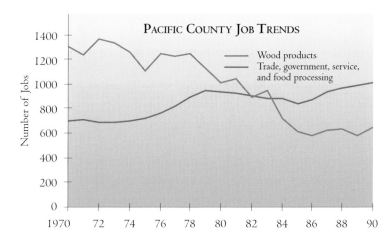

ideal for sustainable enterprises: It profits while enhancing the diversity and productivity of the ecosystem as a whole.

Timberland owners have already modified forest practices to protect forest corridors along streams once scoured by splashdams and to reduce the downstream impacts of logging. Some second-growth forest stands are thinned to let remaining trees grow larger and to improve wildlife forage on the forest floor. Over time, it may make economic and ecological sense to prune young trees in some managed stands to produce higher-quality lumber, to encourage multi-species forests in place of single-species plantations, and to allow some trees to mature beyond the 55-year rotation cycle. Such multi-aged, structurally diverse forests would sustain more kinds of birds, mammals, and other life forms than even-aged tree farms.

At the invitation of a presidential commission, the Weyerhaeuser Company (the largest owner of timberland in the Willapa ecosystem) has proposed to develop a Willapa watershed management plan integrating management of biological diversity with timber production on its private lands. Company scientists plan to survey and describe plant communities, stream habitats, and wildlife composition in the uplands, to cooperate with other resource users to study the productivity of the entire ecosystem, and to apply their findings to company forest management plans. The intent of the effort is to describe the biodiversity of the uplands today and to project likely changes over time.

🌿 *LEFT: In Willapa, the land, the waters, and the lives of people are inseparable.* (STEVE TERRILL)
🌿 *ABOVE: Reforestation brings new life to harvested timberlands.* (DAVE PUTNAM)

Properly regulated, non-timber products like these edible chanterelles have a place in a sustainable forest economy.
(GARY BRAASCH)

Willapa's second-growth forests grow more than timber. The gathering of chanterelles and matsutake mushrooms in late autumn for the regional restaurant trade and for export; collection of sword ferns, salal, and moss for the floral trade; and summer collection of cascara bark used in the manufacture of laxatives illustrate the range of non-timber products from Willapa's forestlands for which markets already exist. Hundreds of small businesses profitably glean such natural products from the timberlands.

A local initiative aimed at restoring Willapa's native chum salmon runs neatly blends economic and ecological goals. Rehabilitating spawning streams and rebuilding the native stock of chum salmon in Willapa's waters would augment the salmon catch, enhance local fisheries, and at the same time help restore the bay's traditional predator-prey balance, with juvenile chum salmon foraging among oyster and eelgrass beds in their accustomed abundance. The young chum salmon would likely remain in the bay from March through August, the months during which the larvae of burrowing shrimp are most abundant, and might help bring shrimp populations back under control. The recovery of salmon and sturgeon populations would open new niches for businesses that enhance ecological resilience in the bay.

Cranberries, the most valuable agricultural crop in the Willapa ecosystem, depend on clean water. Local growers, concerned with water quality, are already using "integrated pest management" (IPM) methods of pest control that combine biological controls such as natural parasites with limited applications of chemical pesticides timed to coincide with vulnerable stages of insect pests' life cycles. Willapa's cranberries command high prices, enabling local growers to prove the worth of innovative methods. The lessons growers learn about blending technology and biological knowledge may prove valuable in efforts to control spartina and burrowing shrimp on the tidelands.

One primary goal of ecologically sound economic development is to add value to natural resources that originate in the ecosystem before they are sold. A manufacturer of high-quality furniture from red alder, a tree species of great ecological value once shunned as a worthless "weed," typifies the "value-added" approach. The exceptional quality of many Willapa products, particularly its fish, shellfish, and cranberries, justifies premium prices. Nowhere in the world can healthier food from land and sea be grown. As the Willapa name gains recognition, markets will begin to respond to its reputation for clean water and overall ecological health.

The infusion of summertime visitors to the Long Beach Peninsula, which can more than triple Willapa's population to 60,000 on summer weekends, creates a challenge and an opportunity. The influx places demands on the economy and the ecosystem far greater than those imposed by permanent residents. If visitors can be enlisted in local efforts to develop sustainable businesses, educated about Washington's most productive ecosystem, and introduced to local efforts to enhance it, they may prove to be both powerful allies of those efforts and a source of investment in Willapa's future.

Keeping Willapa Bay healthy by promoting environmentally sound, sustainable businesses should help dampen the destructive "boom-and-bust" cycles that have buffeted Willapa's communities. The ecosystem and the human communities it supports have undergone extraordinary changes in the last 140 years. Creating a sustainable economy is in a sense a more modest change than the replacement of Willapa's temperate rain-forest wilderness with its contemporary tapestry of farmed trees, fish, and oysters. And yet, choosing sustainability links today's residents to the distant future, and begins work that their grandchildren can continue with pride.

🌿 TOP: *The forest products industry remains a mainstay of the Willapa economy despite changing technologies and markets.* (GARY BRAASCH) 🌿 BOTTOM: *Locally made products, like these cranberry specialities, capture more of the premium value of Willapa resources before they are shipped from the ecosystem.* (SCOTT WELLSANDT)

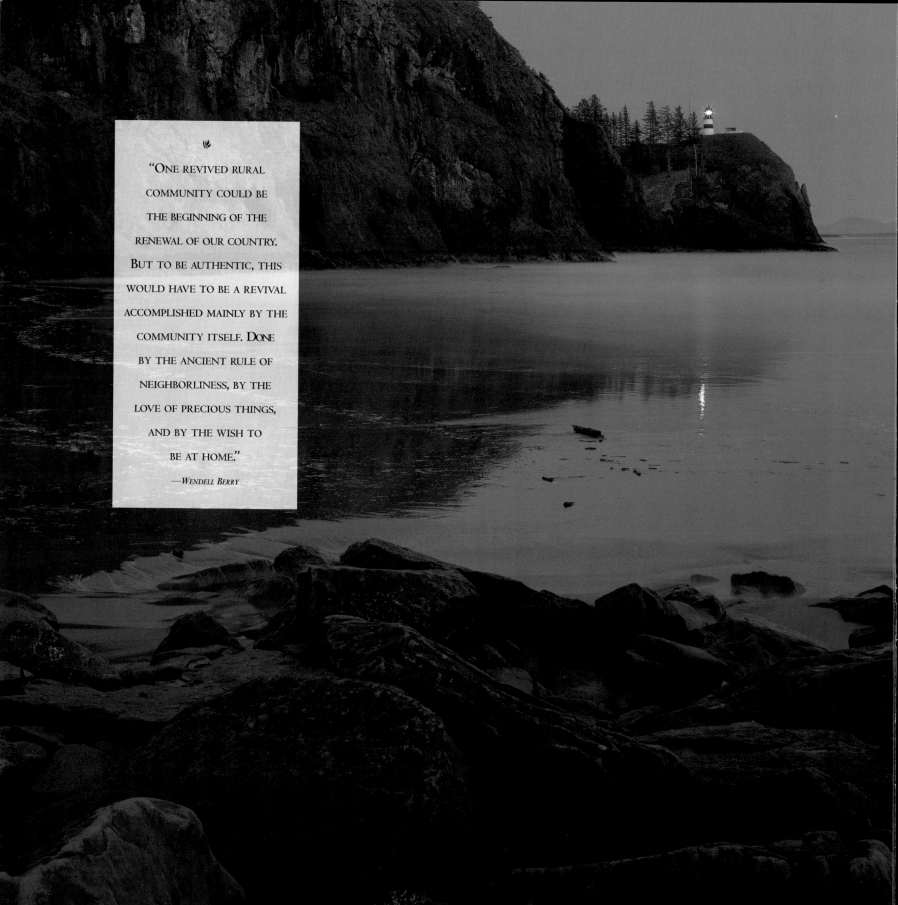

"One revived rural community could be the beginning of the renewal of our country. But to be authentic, this would have to be a revival accomplished mainly by the community itself. Done by the ancient rule of neighborliness, by the love of precious things, and by the wish to be at home."

—Wendell Berry

THE
WILLAPA ALLIANCE

Founded in 1992, The Willapa Alliance is an independent, nonprofit organization dedicated to developing and implementing strategies for sustainable, conservation-based economic development in the Willapa ecosystem. The Alliance is composed of local residents, landowners, and members of the Shoalwater Bay Indian Tribe. The Alliance was created to promote research and understanding of the ecosystem, to support education in the

❧ *LEFT: Evening unfolds over Cape Disappointment.* (STEVE TERRILL) ❧ *ABOVE: The majesty of Willapa's remnant ancient forests can inspire awe.* (GARY BRAASCH)

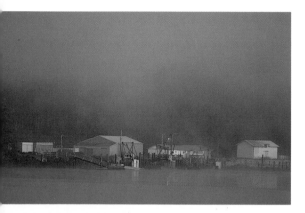

community, to foster communication among its residents and with its visitors, and to encourage local enterprises that conserve and enhance its lands and waters. The mission statement of the Alliance reads:

To enhance the diversity, productivity, and health of Willapa's unique environment, to promote sustainable economic development, and to expand the choices available to the people who live here.

Supporters of the Willapa Alliance include two conservation organizations: Ecotrust of Portland, Oregon, and The Nature Conservancy's Washington Chapter in Seattle. Ecotrust is a nonprofit organization that seeks to integrate conservation and economic development in rural communities by building on local cultural and economic traditions. The Nature Conservancy is a nonprofit conservation organization committed to preserving plants, animals, and ecosystems that represent the diversity of life on earth by protecting the lands and waters they need to survive.

For more information, please write:
The Willapa Alliance
P.O. Box 773
Long Beach, WA 98631

❧ TOP: *Choosing sustainability links Willapa's residents to the future, and begins work that their grandchildren can continue with pride.* (SUNNY WALTER)
❧ BOTTOM: *Fresh herbs gathered in a Willapa garden.* (DOUG PLUMMER) ❧ RIGHT: *The sunset concerto: variations on a theme of land, sea, and sky.* (KEITH LAZELLE)

❧

THE WILLAPA ALLIANCE:

Karen Snyder, Chair	Bob Hitt
Dan'l Markham, Secretary	Elliot Marks
John McMahon, Treasurer	Norris Petit
Spencer B. Beebe	Robert P. Rose
Mason Browne	Herb Whitish
David Campiche	Richard Wilson
Fred Dracobly	Lee Wiegardt

ACKNOWLEDGMENTS

Publishing a book of this scope is truly a team effort. The Willapa Alliance would like to thank many individuals and organizations for the time, skills, and resources that made it possible. The book is based on the original work of Kathleen Sayce and Michael Colby. Kathleen had the vision to produce it book and also contributed original research for the text. The author also consulted the work of Rachel Nugent, Bruce Suzumoto, Harold Seely, Ty Tice, and Louise Forrest during the preparation of *A Tidewater Place.*

Thanks to the following foundations and individuals for their generous financial support of The Willapa Alliance program: the Bullitt Foundation, Meyer Memorial Trust, Weyerhaeuser Company Foundation, Burlington Resources, Ben Cheney Foundation, Ford Foundation, Northwest Area Foundation, Clarence E. Heller Charitable Foundation, Sequoia Foundation, Forest Foundation, Fanwood Foundation/West, Kuyper Foundation, Newman's Own Inc., U.S. Fish and Wildlife Foundation, Foster Foundation, Horizons Foundation, Strong Foundation and Mrs. Ann Lennartz.

Special thanks to the ARCO Foundation for their financial support of *A Tidewater Place* and Simpson Investment Company for donating paper for the cover of the book.

The author and editor are grateful to the members of The Willapa Alliance for their guidance and support throughout the writing and production of this book: Dan'l Markham, David Campiche, Fred Dracobly, Bob Hitt, John McMahon, Bob Rose, Herb Whitish, Dick Wilson, Norris Petit, Mason Browne, John Davis, founding chair Lee Wiegardt, and current chair Karen Snyder, whose direction and comments were invaluable. We would also like to thank Janie Rose, Jan Wilson, Mary Wildhaber, Ardell McPhail, Lydia Murray, C & D Publishing, and Senator Sid Snyder for their help.

In addition, the author wishes to thank Spencer Beebe, Arthur Dye, Erin Kellogg, Alana Probst, and Peter Schoonmaker of Ecotrust and Elliot Marks of The Nature Conservancy for information and inspiration; Gordon Todd of The Nature Conservancy for editorial and logistical support; Chairman Herb Whitish and Ken Hansen of the Shoalwater Bay Indian Tribe for sharing tribal records and heritage; Miranda Wecker for thoughtful reviews; refuge manager Jim Hidy and former naturalist Jim Atkinson of the Willapa National Wildlife Refuge and Jim Rochelle of the Weyerhaeuser Co. for factual information; John Draper and Gloria Parish of Weyerhaeuser for photo assistance; and the staff of the Pacific Northwest Collection at the University of Washington for historical source materials.

Bruce Weilepp of the Pacific County Historical Society, Vickie Hinson and Noreen Robinson of the Ilwaco Heritage Foundation, and Wayne O'Neil of Midway Printery provided valuable help in locating historical photographs of the Willapa area.

The editor would also like to thank Elizabeth Watson for her beautiful graphic design work and dedication to this project, Don Dvorak of United Graphics for his commitment and printing advice, and the photographers who caught the beauty of Willapa in their images.

FURTHER READING

The following publications, some available commercially and some best found at regional libraries, augment this profile of the Willapa ecosystem with much more detail on the natural and human history of Willapa and the coastal Northwest.

Jean Hazeltine. 1956. *Willapa Bay—Its Historical and Regional Geography.* South Bend, Wash.: privately published.

Joel W. Hedgpeth and S. Obrebski. 1981. *"Willapa Bay: A Historical Perspective and a Rationale for Research,"* Washington, D.C.: U.S. Department of the Interior, U.S. Fish and Wildlife Service (FWS/OBS-81/03).

Arthur Kruckeberg. 1991. *The Natural History of Puget Sound Country.* Seattle: University of Washington Press.

Lucile McDonald. 1989. *Coast Country.* Ilwaco, Wash.: Ilwaco Heritage Foundation.

Robert Michael Pyle. 1986. *Wintergreen: Listening to the Land's Heart.* Boston: Houghton Mifflin.

James G. Swan. 1972. *The Northwest Coast or, Three Years Residence in Washington Territory.* Seattle: University of Washington Press (originally published by Harper & Brothers Publishers, 1857).